Richard Scarry's

BEST BEDTIME BOOK EVER

HAMLYN

Contents

Just an Ordinary Day with Babykins	4
Numbers	12
Nursery Rhyme Time	14
Happy Lappy from Finland	16
Two Norwegian Fishermen	18
At the Zoo	20
Nursery Rhyme Time	22
Off We Go!	24
In the Kitchen	26
Nursery Rhyme Time	28
Smokey, the New York Fireman	30
At the Playground	34
Nursery Rhyme Time	36
Sergeant Yukon of the Canadian Mounties	38
Farmer Bear's Farm	40
Hans, the Dutch Plumber	42
Nursery Rhyme Time	44
The Alphabet	46
Babykins' Birthday	48
Ah-Choo of Hong Kong	50
Nursery Rhyme Time	52
Mario, the Venetian Gondolier	54
Mr Fixit Fox around the House	58
Shapes and Sizes	60
The Baby	61
Nursery Rhyme Time	62
Cucumber, the African Photographer	64
The Pig Family	66
Nursery Rhyme Time	69
Manuel of Mexico	70
Spring	72

Summer 73
Autumn 74
Winter 75
Nursery Rhyme Time 76
Albert, the Belgian Barge Captain 78
Nicky visits the Doctor 80
Nursery Rhyme Time 82
Sneef, the Best Detective in Europe 86
Dr Krunchchew of Russia 88
Nursery Rhyme Time 90
Glip and Glop, the Greek Painters 92
The Bear Twins get Dressed 94
Nursery Rhyme Time 96
Professor Dig and his Egyptian Mummy 98
Sven Svenson's Busy Day 100
Nursery Rhyme Time 102
Mamma Bear bakes a Cake 104
Ukulele Louie, the Hawaiian Fisherman 106
Nursery Rhyme Time 108
Cleaning-Up Time 110
Angus, the Scottish Bagpiper 112
Nursery Rhyme Time 114
The Silly Polish Farmers 116
Out West 118
Nursery Rhyme Time 120
Schmudge, the German Chimney Sweep 122
Ernst, the Swiss Mountain Climber 124
Nursery Rhyme Time 126
Good Night 128

Just an Ordinary Day with Babykins

When the alarm clock goes off in the morning, Father Cat jumps out of bed.

Babykins is already awake.

Here he is, all washed and ready for breakfast. My, what a fine fellow!

Babykins likes to have breakfast with Father. Father likes to have breakfast with his newspaper. Oops! Be careful, Father! You're spilling the milk!

Mother Cat can pour four cups of coffee at once, three for Father and one for herself.

Oh, oh, Father. There's no time to drink your last cup of coffee. You are going to be late for your train.

Father Cat finishes his breakfast while running to catch his train.

Hurry, Father. Faster, faster. He runs, he leaps . . .

Thump! He misses his train!

Luckily a bus comes along. Father manages to catch it.

But he can't find his ticket. Where do you suppose he put it? Poor Father. Will he ever get to work?

Meanwhile, at home, Mother Cat is trying to get Babykins dressed. But that little rascal wants to play with his hammer. "Babykins!" says Mother. "Please sit still while I tuck in your shirt."

Now Babykins is dressed in his nice clean clothes. He is trying to copy the television commercial. Quick, Kitty, turn around!

Today the Cats are having stew for lunch. Babykins loves stew. He loves to wear it on his head.

I think that this must be the only neat way to feed Babykins. Good for you, Kitty!

It is bathtime! That's why Mother has her raincoat on. She is going to give Babykins his bath. Look out, Babykins! Mother is after you.

Now Babykins is all nice and clean. Look out, Mother! You should have kept your raincoat on.

At last Babykins is ready for his nap. Sleep well, Babykins. You're such a good little boy when you're asleep.

Be quiet, Tom! Babykins is trying to sleep. RRRRRRRRR!! Tom is cleaning the rug with the vacuum cleaner.

Grandma doesn't want Tom and Kitty to wake Babykins, so she has taken them to the toy shop. She is going to buy them each a present for helping her around the house.

Oh, what a beautiful tuba
Tom has found!

Grandma is getting her money to pay
for the tuba. Tom, come out of there
this instant!

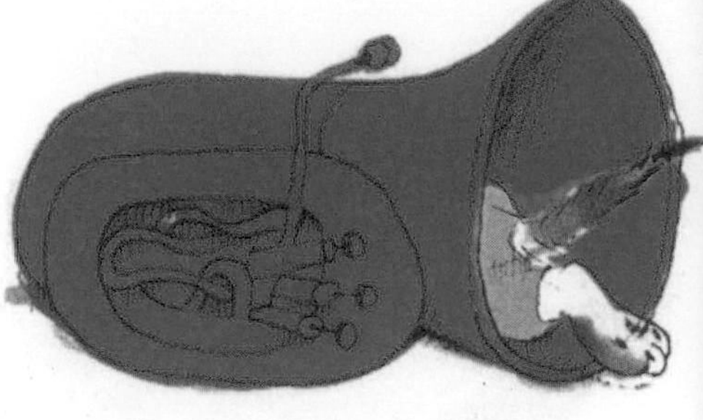

Kitty has found the present
she wants, too.
"Oh, Kitty," says Grandma.
"Did you have to pick
the biggest doll in the shop?"

Poor Grandma had to
carry those big presents
all the way home. She is
all worn out. She's sleeping
now, but Babykins is awake!
No, Babykins, no . . .

BLAAAAT! Oh, Babykins,
I didn't know you could
play the tuba.

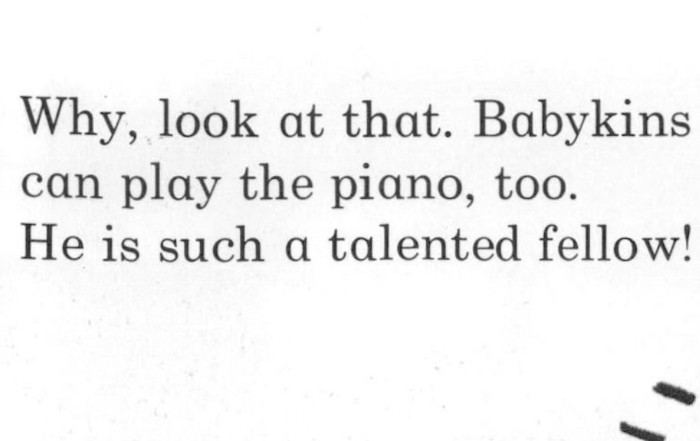

Why, look at that. Babykins
can play the piano, too.
He is such a talented fellow!

Tom is playing with Babykins
to keep him out of trouble.
What fine musicians!

"All right, boys," says Mother.
That is enough music for one day.
Why don't you do something
quiet?"
So Tom and Babykins decide to
build with their blocks. What a
wonderful tower they have made.
What will they think of next?

They've thought of
building a wall! Now they
will have to think of a
way for Father to get in
the door.
CRASH! They thought
of a way.

After a hard day's work, Father relaxes with his paper. Babykins relaxes with Father's watch.

Babykins is a curious little fellow. He likes to find out how things work.

No, Babykins, a watch does not work like that. Oh, that rascal Babykins. He has broken Father's watch!

After supper, Father settles down with his paper again. Mother turns on the light. Tom and Kitty are doing their homework. But where is Babykins?

Here he is, the little rascal. He wants to play with Father.

Poor Father is too tired. He wants to take a nap. I think you should stop that right now, Babykins!

At last Father is awake. Now he's trying to watch television. And Babykins is still climbing about.

It is just before bedtime. Father always reads a good-night story to Babykins. Babykins just loves a good story.

And so – off to bed goes Babykins. Goodnight, Babykins. Sleep tight.

Aaah. At last Babykins is in bed. Now everyone can relax. But wait a minute. What's that noise I hear? Oh, no . . . Babykins wants a glass of water!

Here is Babykins sound asleep at last. Sweet little Babykins. He's such a good little baby. Sleep tight, Babykins.

Numbers

How high can you count?
Can you count up to
twenty ladybirds?
I'll bet you can.

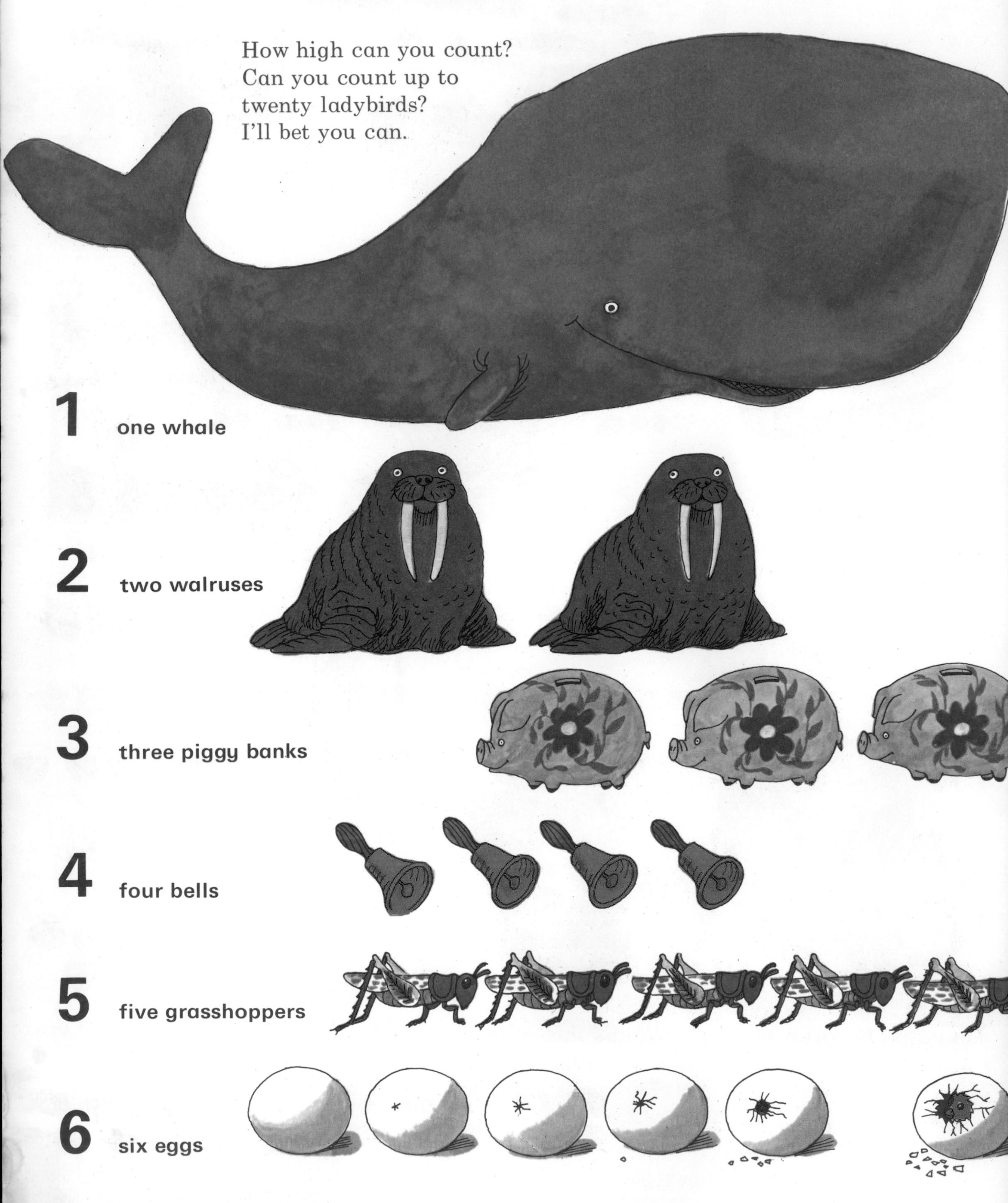

1 one whale

2 two walruses

3 three piggy banks

4 four bells

5 five grasshoppers

6 six eggs

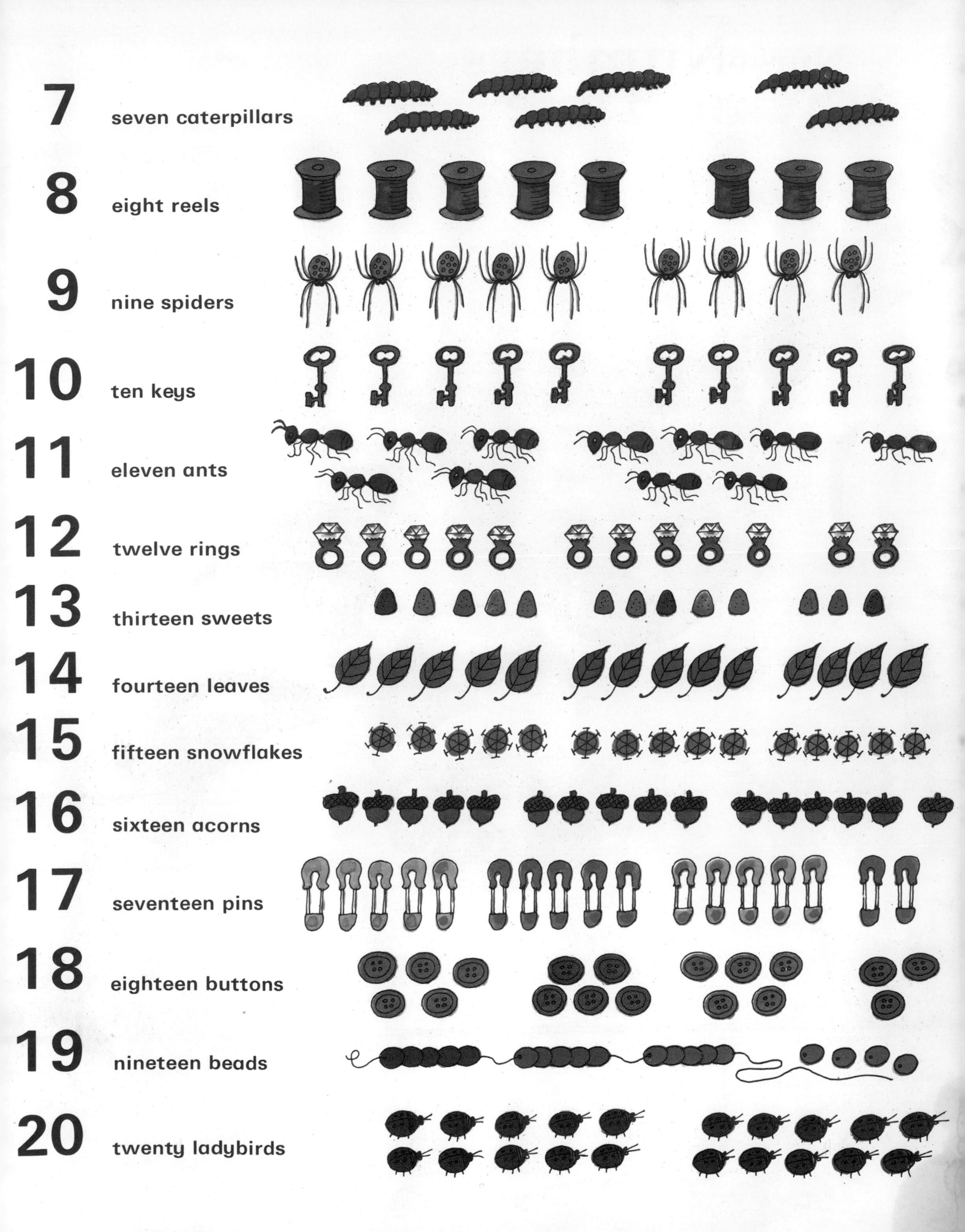
7 seven caterpillars
8 eight reels
9 nine spiders
10 ten keys
11 eleven ants
12 twelve rings
13 thirteen sweets
14 fourteen leaves
15 fifteen snowflakes
16 sixteen acorns
17 seventeen pins
18 eighteen buttons
19 nineteen beads
20 twenty ladybirds

Nursery
Rhyme Time

Polly, put the kettle on,
Polly, put the kettle on,
Polly, put the kettle on,
We'll all have tea.

Sukey, take it off again,
Sukey, take it off again,
Sukey, take it off again,
They've all gone away.

Happy Lappy from Finland

Happy Lappy lives in the far north of Finland.

Happy Lappy's father takes care of Santa Claus' reindeer. Just before Christmas every year, he lassoes the reindeer and takes them to Santa.

The reindeer are very strong, and Lappy is too small to lasso them.

"When you are big and strong," his father told him, "you will lasso the reindeer for Santa." To be ready when that day comes, Lappy practises with his rope.

Lappy's sister holds two branches to her head. She pretends she is a reindeer. Lappy chases her. Just as she disappears over the hill, Lappy throws his lasso. He has lassoed her.

But no! He has lassoed one of Santa's reindeer and that reindeer didn't want to be lassoed.

Away he ran, with Lappy holding on tight.

Around and around in circles he ran . . . but Lappy didn't let go.

After a while that reindeer was so tired he could run no more.

Lappy's father was so pleased.

"You are now big and strong enough to lasso Santa's reindeer," he said. "From now on you will take care of them. Come along now. We must take the reindeer to Santa. Perhaps he will have a toy for each of you."

Sure enough, Santa did. Lappy and his sister were very happy.

Two Norwegian Fishermen

Uncle Olaf and Uncle Oscar had nine nieces and nephews waiting for them on the dock. They were waiting for Uncle Olaf and Uncle Oscar to catch a big fish for supper.

Uncle Olaf caught a tin can.
Uncle Oscar didn't catch anything.

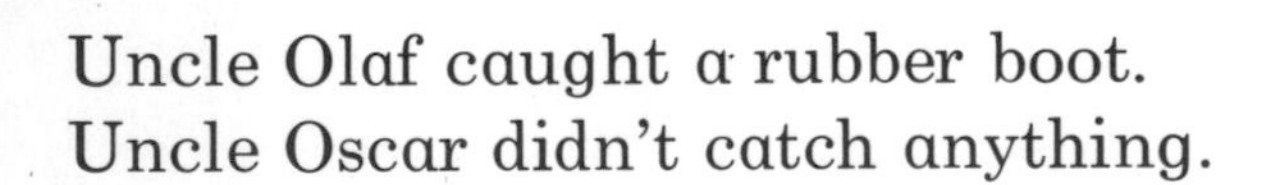

Uncle Olaf caught a rubber boot.
Uncle Oscar didn't catch anything.

Uncle Olaf caught an old tyre.
Uncle Oscar didn't catch anything.
What kind of a fisherman is Uncle Oscar anyway? He can't catch anything.

WOW!! Uncle Oscar caught a fish.

He paddled back to the dock where the nine nieces and nephews were waiting . . .

. . . and that night, they had the best fish supper ever!

deer
lion
elephant
tiger
panda
monkeys
brown bear
gorilla
polar bear

At the Zoo

Mr and Mrs Mouse took
their children to the zoo.
How will those children
ever be able to get
all those balloons
into their house tonight?
Which is your favourite animal
at the zoo?

This little pig went to market,

This little pig stayed at home,

This little pig had roast beef,

This little pig had none,

And this little pig cried, "Wee-wee-wee-wee-wee,
I can't find my way home."

Nursery
Rhyme Time

Old King Cole
  Was a merry old soul,
And a merry old soul was he;
  He called for his pipe,
  And he called for his bowl,
And he called for his fiddlers three.

  Every fiddler, he had a fiddle,
  And a very fine fiddle had he;
Twee tweedle dee, tweedle dee, went the fiddlers
  Oh, there's none so rare
  As can compare
With King Cole and his fiddlers three.

Off We Go!

Beep, beep! Beep, beep!
"Move over, Squeaky," barks Dingo. "I want to pass."
Dingo likes to go in his car, and he likes to go very fast.

Some police officers have cars and some ride motorcycles.
Oops! This police officer has stopped Dingo for speeding.

People who don't have a car can go on a bus. Andy sits on the top deck because he likes to feel the rain on his snout.

Some people like to take a taxi. Pappa Bear is taking the taxi door. No, Pappa, that is not what we mean by "take a taxi".

When a car won't go, Mr Fixit Fox tows it away with his breakdown lorry.

"Help!" cries Dingo, as his car is flattened by a dustcart and a tractor. How ever did that happen? I think Dingo will be needing Mr Fixit Fox and his breakdown lorry.

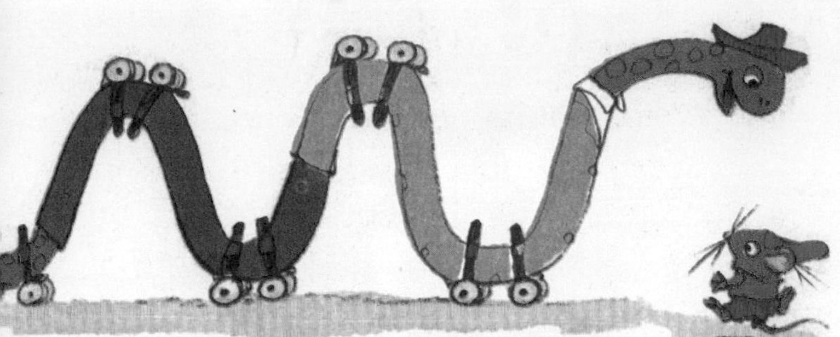

Have you ever seen a snake roller-skating? Squigley does it very well. He needs lots of skates because he wears one on each wiggle.

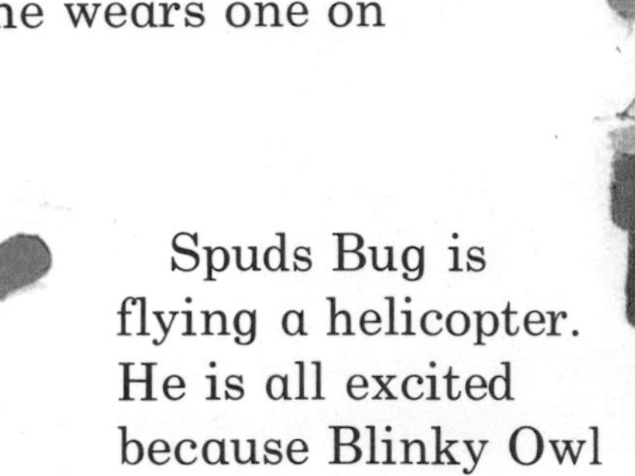

Spuds Bug is flying a helicopter. He is all excited because Blinky Owl is trying out his new invention—the Hootcopter. Will it fly?

Sneakers can go in the deep snow because he is wearing snowshoes.

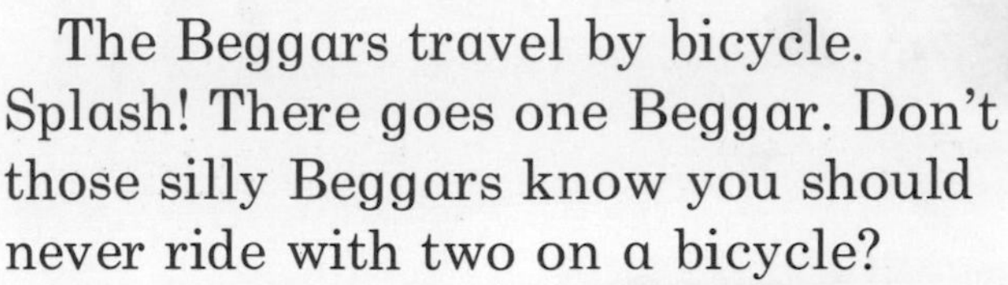

The Beggars travel by bicycle. Splash! There goes one Beggar. Don't those silly Beggars know you should never ride with two on a bicycle?

Baron von Crow zooms into the air in his plane. "Let's go, Blinky," he caws. "I'll race you to Paris."

Skiing is another good way to get about in the snow, if you know how.

"But it looked so easy," sighs Bumbles.

Perhaps Macintosh can give him a few tips.

kitchen cabinet
refrigerator
tin open
soap
teapot
power point
work surface
freezer
dishwashe
dustbin
washing machine
egg whisk
laundry basket
mixing bowl
stool
spoon
measuring jug
rolling pin
biscuit cutter
dough
strainer
funnel
cake tin
baking tray
sauce bottle
slice
sugar bowl
mustard pot
mincer

In the Kitchen

All the little piglets like to help their mother in the kitchen. They are making good things to eat. What is Mother Pig putting into the oven?

Nursery Rhyme Time

Barber, barber, shave a pig,
How many hairs to make a wig?
Four and twenty, that's enough.
Give the barber a pinch of snuff.

Peter Piper picked a peck of pickled peppers;
A peck of pickled peppers Peter Piper picked.
If Peter Piper picked a peck of pickled peppers,
Where's the peck of pickled peppers Peter Piper picked?

Smokey, the New York Fireman

Smokey was taking a nap in his fire station.

Look! There is smoke coming from Kathleen Kitty's window!

The fire alarm rang! BRRRRRRRRRRRRINNNNNNGGGGGG!!

Smokey put on his hat, his boots and his raincoat.

He slid down a pole into his fire engine below.

Clang! Clang! Get out of the way!
Officer Murphy stopped the cars.

A pie van didn't get out of the way in time.

The sky was full of blueberry pies . . . and the pieman!

Kathleen Kitty was screaming to be saved.

Smokey climbed up the ladder and saved her.

He turned his hose on the fire
SWOOOOOOOOOOSH!
and the fire was out.

He turned his hose on his fire engine. SWOOOOOOOOSH! and his fire engine was red again.

He turned his hose on the pieman. SWOOOOOOOOOOOSH! and the pieman was clean again.

Then they all went inside to see what the fire was all about. It was a blueberry pie which had burnt in the oven.

So Kathleen Kitty made another . . .

. . . and they all sat down and ate it.

At the Playground

The children are all having fun doing different things. Which children are doing the things you like best?

kite
jungle gym
bubble blowing
merry-go-round
tag
tossing the ring
hoop rolling
jacks
marbles
sand pit
kite string
bouncing ball
hopscotch
4
7
3
2
6
5
8

Tom, Tom, the piper's son,
Stole a pig and away did run.
The pig was eat, and Tom was beat,
And Tom went crying down the street.

Nursery Rhyme Time

There was an old crow
Sat upon a clod,
That's the end of my song,
—That's odd.

Diddle, diddle, dumpling, my son John,
Went to bed with his trousers on;
One shoe off, and one shoe on;
Diddle, diddle, dumpling, my son John.

Jack, be nimble,
Jack, be quick,
Jack, jump over
The candlestick.

Hush-a-bye, baby, on the tree top,
When the wind blows the cradle will rock,
When the bough breaks the cradle will fall,
Down will come baby, cradle, and all.

Hickety, pickety, my black hen,
She lays eggs for gentlemen;
Gentlemen come every day
To see what my black hen doth lay.
Sometimes nine and sometimes ten,
Hickety, pickety, my black hen.

Sergeant Yukon of the Canadian Mounties

It was a peaceful day in Goldtown away up in the Canadian Northwest. The door to Sergeant Yukon's police station suddenly flew open.

"Klondike Kid and Tundra Pete are back in town!" said Grubstake Moose.
That meant trouble, for they were the two nastiest men in all Canada.

Sergeant Yukon ran to the door and looked out.
Everyone was running down the street as fast as he could go. Everyone was afraid of these two bullies.

But Sergeant Yukon wasn't afraid.
"I shall take care of them," he said to himself as he marched bravely up the street.

Just look at that ugly Klondike Kid. He has taken a lollipop away from a little girl and she is crying.

And just look at that nasty Tundra Pete, splashing that nice old lady's dress.

Oh. Doesn't he think he's funny!

"You are both mean bullies," said Sergeant Yukon. "I am taking you to jail." But look out, Sergeant Yukon! I think they mean to hit you!

Sergeant Yukon ducked just in time.

Sergeant Yukon dragged them off to jail. And they stayed there until they learned not to be bullies any more.

crow
weather vane
scarecrow
plough
field
tractor
hayloft
barn
goat
stall
tin can
milk churn
bucket
cart
truck
hen
cock
pigsty
chick
dog kennel

Farmer Bear's Farm

Farmer Bear has a very busy farm.
What is Mrs Bear doing? What is the horse doing?
What is the duck doing?
What is the scarecrow
supposed to be doing? He is
not doing it, is he?

Hans, the Dutch Plumber

Hans lived in Holland. Somehow or other Hans always managed to come home from work soaking wet. This made his wife very angry.

Sometimes he would get wet because he forgot his umbrella.

Sometimes he would get wet mending a leaky pipe.

But he really got wet when he didn't look where he was going and fell into a canal.

Now much of the land of Holland is below the level of the sea. The people built dikes to keep the sea water out. If a dike was to get a hole in it, the water would pour through the hole and all the land would be covered with water and fish.

One day Hans saw a big leak in the dike. There was water pouring through it. A tourist was waiting to take a picture of someone putting something in the hole to stop the leak in the dike.

Hans put the tourist in the hole to stop the leak in the dike. Now a tourist is not the best thing for mending leaks so Hans rode off to get some bags of sand. When he returned he took the tourist out of the hole and filled the hole with bags of sand.

The burgomaster gave Hans a medal. His wife would be very pleased. He had mended the biggest leak ever and he hadn't got the littlest bit wet.

On his way home it started to rain. He had remembered to bring his umbrella. He would arrive home nice and dry. Today his wife wouldn't be angry with him.

But wait! Hans doesn't see that the bridge is open!

His wife is very angry.

Nursery Rhyme Time

Blow, wind blow! And go, mill, go!
That the miller may grind his corn;
That the baker may take it,
And into bread make it,
And bring us a loaf in the morn.

The Alphabet

The alligator is eating an apple.
The goose is wearing gloves.
What is the Indian eating?

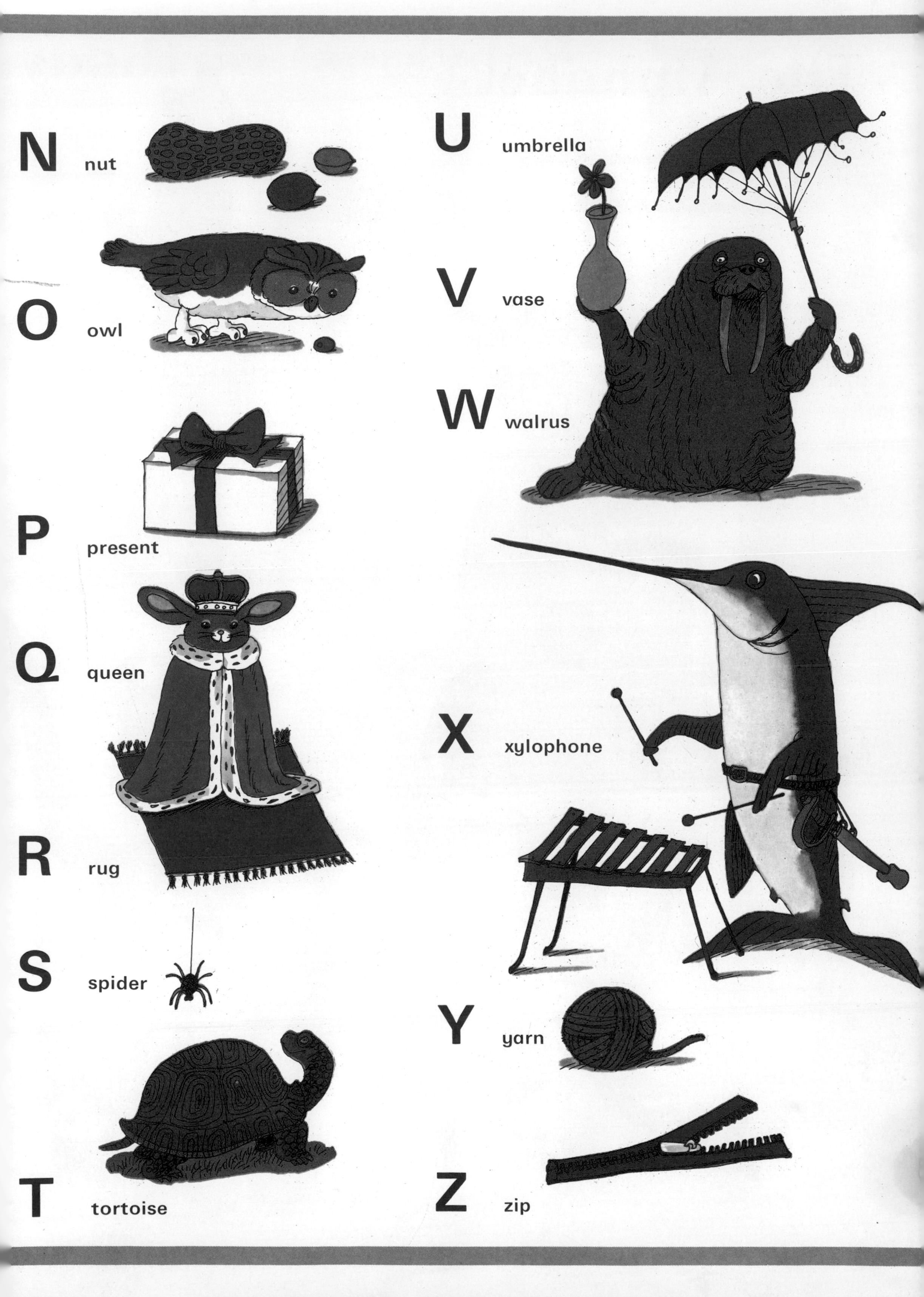
N nut
O owl
P present
Q queen
R rug
S spider
T tortoise
U umbrella
V vase
W walrus
X xylophone
Y yarn
Z zip

Babykins' Birthday

Babykins is writing the invitations to his birthday party.

Guess how old he will be?

Babykins is all dressed up for the party. He is wearing his new clothes . . . and chocolate and vanilla ice cream.

The party has begun. I think Squeaky's balloon is a little too big for him.

Tom plays "Happy Birthday to Babykins" on his funny horn.

As Tom calls everyone to the table, a neighbour rings the doorbell to complain about all the noise.

Kitty wants her dolls to have some birthday cake, too. "Here, you carry this one," she says to Flossie.

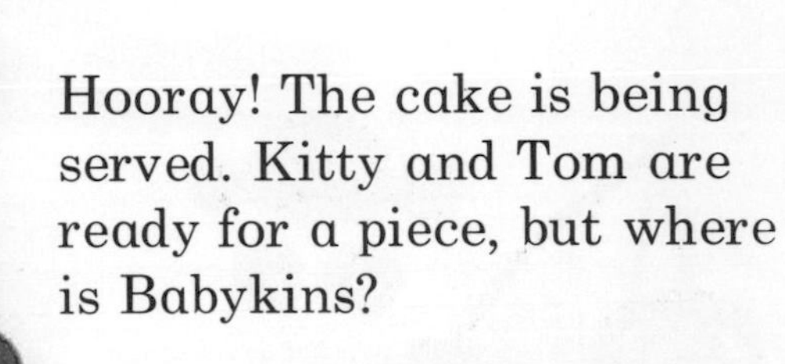

Hooray! The cake is being served. Kitty and Tom are ready for a piece, but where is Babykins?

Here he is, the funny fellow. He is entertaining his guests with some tricks.

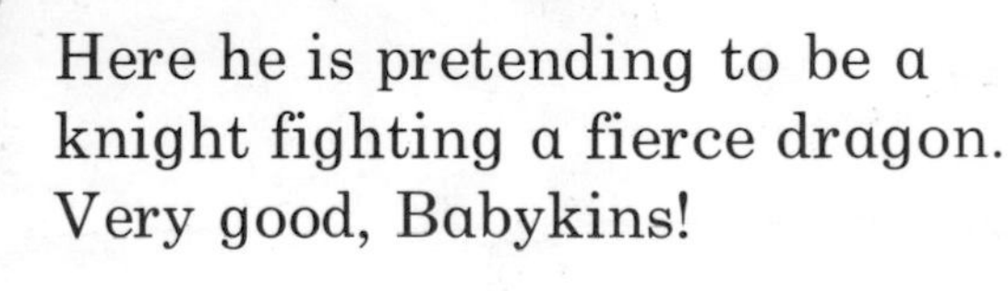

Here he is pretending to be a knight fighting a fierce dragon. Very good, Babykins!

Here is Babykins balancing a dish. What skill! What daring!

What happened?

Ah-Choo of Hong Kong

Ah-Choo had a nose
that sometimes tickled.

And when it tickled
Ah-Choo sneezed.
AH-CHOOOO!

And when he sneezed
terrible things happened.

Ah-Choo was bringing home two baskets of eggs. He looked to see if he had broken any. No. He hadn't.

His nose tickled again.

Ah-Choo sneezed even louder.
AH-CHOO.

Ah-Choo's eggs didn't break.
But his nose did tickle again.

AH-CHOO!

It is lucky that no one was hurt.
It is lucky the eggs didn't break.

Ah-Choo finally arrived home. Mama and Baby Ah-Choo were waiting. Mama Ah-Choo had her cooking pot on the stove. She was going to cook hard-boiled eggs for supper.

Then what do you think happened!
Baby Ah-Choo sneezed a tiny AH-CHOO!

"I think that for supper we will have dropped-egg soup instead!" said Mama Ah-Choo.

Nursery Rhyme Time

There was an old woman who lived in a shoe,
She had so many children she didn't know what
to do.
She gave them some broth without any bread;
She whipped them all soundly and put them
to bed.

Mario, the Venetian Gondolier

Mario had a melon boat. Now, a melon boat is very useful, but it is not beautiful, like a gondola. Mario worked hard selling melons, so that one day he would have enough money to buy a beautiful gondola.

"Just look at that pretty gondola all decorated with flowers," he said to himself. "It must be going to a wedding."

Sure enough! The gondola stopped at a palace. Tina, who was a very beautiful princess, came out with her father. The gondola would take her to church to be married.

Oh! What a shame! Tina is too big for the gondola! How will she ever get to the church to be married?

Have no fear. Here comes Mario! He is strong because he is always lifting melons. He lifts Tina and her father into his boat.

Mario rowed them to the church. Everyone thought it was very funny to see all the melons going to a wedding.

Tina was married to Toni. She was so happy she kissed Toni. Tina's father was so happy he kissed Mario. If it hadn't been for Mario there would have been no wedding.

Tina's father gave Mario a shiny new gondola as a present. Mario put his melon boat away in his cellar. He is now a real gondolier. He sings happily as he paddles along the Grand Canal on romantic moonlight nights. But whenever there is a holiday Mario brings out his melon boat.

For you see . . .

. . . Tina and Toni now have lots of children, and they need a strong and sturdy boat to carry them. Yes! A very strong and sturdy boat!

Mr Fixit Fox around the House

Mr Fixit Fox is handy to have around the house. He can fix anything.
He can fix a typewriter with a single bash.

He can fix a radio.

Why Mr Fixit! You never told us you were going to be on television.

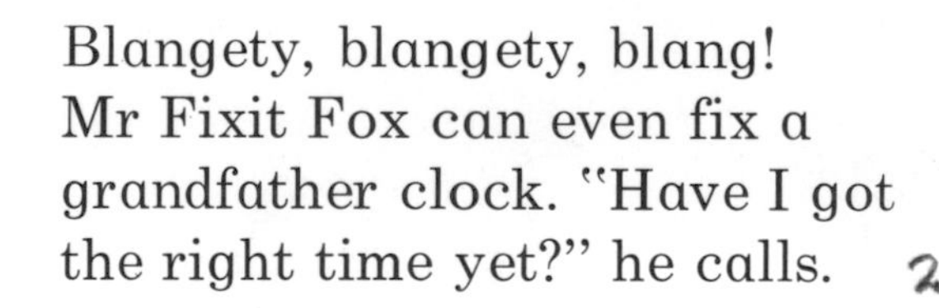

Blangety, blangety, blang!
Mr Fixit Fox can even fix a grandfather clock. "Have I got the right time yet?" he calls.

Chips is good at fixing children's toys. Look at him go. That Chips is certainly a hard worker!

Mr Fixit Fox and Chips are going to fix this tricycle. Just a little twist here, and a big blam there, and it'll be as good as new. (I hope.)

Once Mr Fixit Fox even fixed Mamma Bear's stove.

Everything was fine until she tried to use it.

Mr Fixit Fox had to buy Mamma a new stove. Well! I don't think I'll ask Mr Fixit Fox to fix any of *my* things!

Shapes and Sizes

The Baby

The Cat family has a new baby kitten.
They don't know what to name it.
What would you like
to name the new baby?
Write the kitten's name here.

TÍCO ___ ___ ___ ___ ___ ___

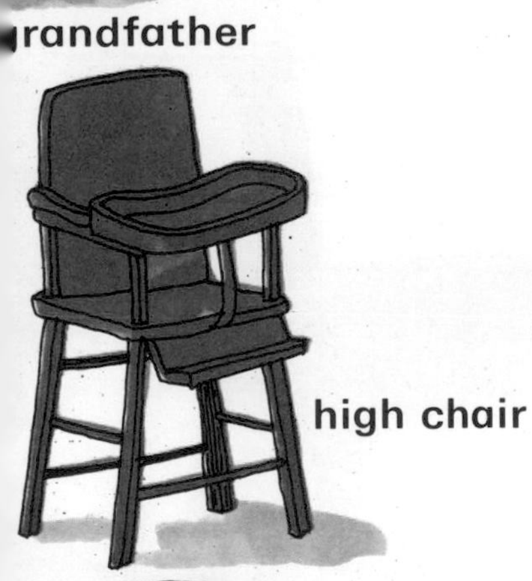

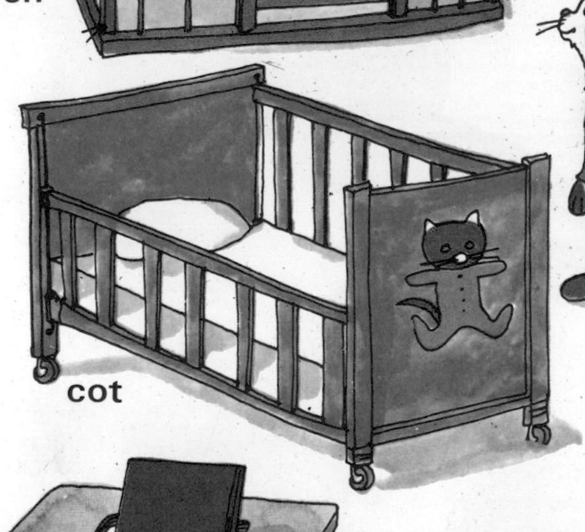

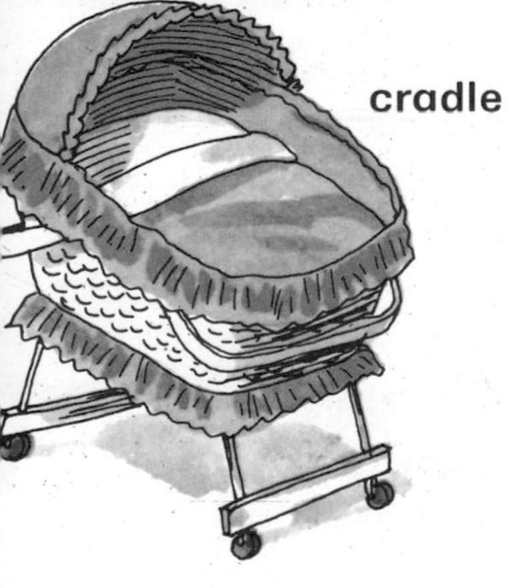

Nursery
Rhyme Time

Peter, Peter, pumpkin eater,
Had a wife and couldn't keep her.
He put her in a pumpkin shell
And there he kept her very well.

Cucumber, the African Photographer

Cucumber took pictures of wild giraffes, and wild zebras, and other wild animals. But he never took pictures of wild lions. Why? Because he was afraid of them!

One day he said, "Goodbye," to his wife and drove far out across the plains to photograph wild zebras with his movie camera.

When night-time came he set up his tent. After he had eaten his supper and played a few songs on his banjo, he went to sleep.

Cucumber had not been asleep long when some wild animals came into his tent. WILD LIONS!!!
"Look at that sweet doll," said the little girl lion.

"I wonder what this machine is?" said Father Lion.

He pressed a button and the camera started to work.

WHRRRRRRrrrrrrrr!

Then he picked up Cucumber's banjo and started to sing.

The little girl lion picked up Cucumber, and started to dance.

Cucumber was sound asleep.

The twin baby lions started to cry.

"Put the doll back in the bed," roared Mother Lion. "It is time we were leaving."

The little girl lion put Cucumber back in his bed. Even with all that noise and everything, Cucumber didn't wake up.

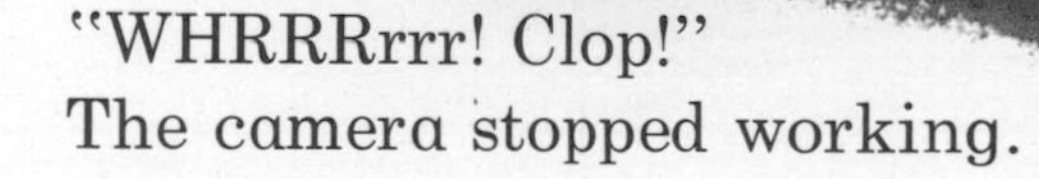

"WHRRRrrr! Clop!"
The camera stopped working.

In the morning Cucumber drove home.

What a surprise, when he showed his wife the moving pictures!

"Why, you were only pretending!" said Mrs Cucumber. "You're not afraid of wild lions after all!"

And Cucumber never was after that.

The Pig Family

Pa

Pickles

Ma

The Piglets

Here is the Pig Family—
Pa and Ma and their children
Pickles and the Piglets.

Pickles is smiling because he is eating his favourite pie.

Why are those silly Piglets crying? We shall see.

Pa Pig is a barber. His first customer this afternoon is Brambles Warthog. "Just a little off the sides, please," says Brambles.

Pa gets started, but he can't take his eyes off the "Pig Parade" on television.

Oh, Pa!
What have
you done?

Here are Pa's next customers. Why, it's his own little Piglets!

Why are those silly Piglets crying? Don't they know a haircut doesn't hurt?

Ma says, "You naughty rascal, Pickles. Go to bed right away, without your supper!"

Ma makes supper for herself, Pa, and the Piglets.

Hey, Ma, what's that boot doing in the turnip stew?

Here comes Pa, home from the barber shop. He has brought Ma some roses.
Whoops! Watch your step, Pa!
"Oh dear," says Ma.

Supper is over. "Now where are those Piglets?" says Ma. "It's time for their bath."
Can you find those naughty Piglets?

Now Ma has found them. Why are those silly Piglets crying? Don't they know a bath doesn't hurt?

This Piglet is all clean and dry. Why is he still crying?
Because it's time for bed.

Well, those Piglets have finally stopped crying!
Good night, Piglets.

Nursery Rhyme Time

Rub-a-dub-dub,
Three men in a tub;
And who do you think they be?
The butcher, the baker,
The candlestick-maker;
Turn 'em out, knaves all three!

Manuel of Mexico

Manuel's wife broke her cooking pot. She needed a new pot to cook her beans in for supper.

"Manuel," she said. "Take this money and go to the market place. Buy a new cooking pot so that you may have hot beans for supper."

Manuel was so excited to be going to the market place. He didn't look where he was going. He kicked a cooking pot by accident and broke it. He paid the man for breaking it.

Pig Lady was cooking beans in her cooking pot. He stepped into the stew by mistake. He said he was sorry.

The smell of Pig Lady's beans made him hungry. He went to Armadillo's restaurant and had a bowl of beans.

When he had finished he accidentally knocked over the bean pot and spilled the beans.

"I think it is time to go home," he said to himself. "I think I am forgetting something but I can't remember what."

He didn't look where he was going and bumped into Dog.

A pot landed on his head. "Ah, yes, I remember now. I was to buy a cooking pot," Manuel said to himself.

But alas! The pot was stuck on his head.

He went home to his wife.

"I remembered to bring home a cooking pot," he said.

His wife had to break the pot to get it off his head.

Manuel had cold beans for supper.

Spring

Look at that baby lamb hop!
It is spring. He is happy.
Look at Mr Bear coming out of
his cave! It is spring.
Now he can use his new
lawn mower.

Summer

Do you like to go
on picnics in the summer-time?
Ants just love to go to picnics.
Do you know why?

Autumn

In the autumn the air gets colder. The green leaves turn to bright colours. Then they fall to the ground. Who is raking them all up?

Winter
There are many ways to have fun on the snow and ice. Maybe you would like to do all of them. Would you?
snowstorm
sleigh
icicle
skis
sledge
toboggan
ice fishing
ice skating rink
snowball
ice hockey stick
puck
scarf
ice skates
jeep
snow plough
a pig all wrapped up
snowman

Nursery Rhyme Time

Simple Simon met a pieman,
Going to the fair.
Said Simple Simon to the pieman,
"Please let me taste your ware."

Said the pieman to Simple Simon,
"Show me first your penny."
Said Simple Simon to the pieman,
"Indeed, I have not any."

Albert, the Belgian Barge Captain

Albert's barge was sailing merrily along the canal. Albert's wife was putting the washing on the line.

Pieter Pig was dreaming of catching a big fish.

"A fish! A fish! I've caught a fish!" said the pig.

"You've caught a barge captain!" said Albert. "Now how will I ever get back on my barge?"

"There is only one way," said Pieter Pig.
"This is the way . . .

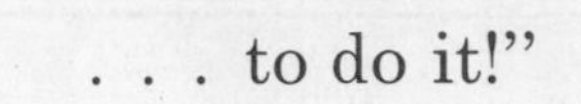

. . . to do it!"

Albert's trousers tore.

And Albert landed, upside down, in his pyjama trousers!

"Why are you wearing your pyjamas in the middle of the day?" his wife asked him. "And how *ever* did you tear your nice new trousers?"

Nicky visits the Doctor

Nicky's mother is taking him to the doctor.
Say what is happening in each picture.

Nursery Rhyme Time

This is the house that Jack built.

This is the malt
That lay in the house
that Jack built.

This is the rat
That ate the malt
That lay in the house
that Jack built.

This is the cat
That killed the rat
That ate the malt
That lay in the house
that Jack built.

This is the dog
That chased the cat
That killed the rat
That ate the malt
That lay in the house
that Jack built.

This is the cow with
the crumpled horn,
That tossed the dog
That chased the cat
That killed the rat
That ate the malt
That lay in the house
that Jack built.

This is the maid all forlorn,
That milked the cow with
the crumpled horn,
That tossed the dog
That worried the cat
That killed the rat
That ate the malt
That lay in the house
that Jack built.

This is the man all tattered and torn,
That kissed the maiden all forlorn,
That milked the cow with
the crumpled horn,
That tossed the dog
That worried the cat
That killed the rat
That ate the malt
That lay in the house that Jack built.

This is the priest all shaven
and shorn,
That married the man
all tattered and torn,
That kissed the maiden
all forlorn,
That milked the cow
with the crumpled horn,
That tossed the dog
That worried the cat
That killed the rat
That ate the malt
That lay in the house
that Jack built.

This is the cock that crowed
in the morn,
That waked the priest
all shaven and shorn,
That married the man
all tattered and torn,
That kissed the maiden
all forlorn,
That milked the cow
with the crumpled horn,
That tossed the dog
That worried the cat
That killed the rat
That ate the malt
That lay in the house
that Jack built.

This is the farmer sowing
the corn,
That kept the cock
that crowed in the mor
That waked the priest
all shaven and shorn,
That married the man
all tattered and torn,
That kissed the maiden a
forlorn,
That milked the cow
with the crumpled horn
That tossed the dog
That worried the cat
That killed the rat
That ate the malt
That lay in the house
that Jack built.

One, two,
Buckle my shoe,

Three, four,
Knock at the door,

Five, six,
Pick up sticks,

Seven, eight,
Lay them straight,

Nine, ten,
A big fat hen.

There was a crooked man, and he walked a crooked mile,
He found a crooked sixpence against a crooked stile,
He bought a crooked cat, which caught a crooked mouse,
And they all lived together in a little crooked house.

Sneef, the Best Detective in Europe

Sneef was the best detective in all Europe. He was always ready to help Police Chiefs at any time and in any place.

One rainy day in Paris, Sneef received a phone call from the Chief of Police of Nice. He wanted Sneef to come right away.

Oh! How sad. Tomorrow would be Sneef's birthday and he had hoped to spend it at home eating ice cream and cake.

He ran all the way to the train.

"I wonder who all those bad-looking men are?" said Sneef to himself as the train conductor showed him to his bedroom.

"They seem to be watching me!" Sneef was a little frightened.

At every station they stopped at that night, Sneef could see more evil-looking men getting on the train.

And they all carried violin cases! What mischief were they up to?

Sneef was very frightened! He shivered and hid under the bed.

The train arrived in Nice in the morning. Sneef crawled out from under the bed and saw those mysterious men looking at him.

Before he got off the train he put on sunglasses to protect his eyes from the bright sunlight.

When he stepped off the train what do you suppose he saw? Why, he saw all the Police Chiefs of Europe!

They had thrown away their disguises and were playing on their violins.

They were playing, "Happy Birthday to You, Dear Sneefy!"

It was a surprise birthday party!

They all went to the beach and ate ice cream and cake until they could eat no more.

It was Sneef's best birthday party ever!

Dr Krunchchew of Russia

On Monday Dr Krunchchew examined Lion's teeth.

On Tuesday he examined Alligator's teeth.

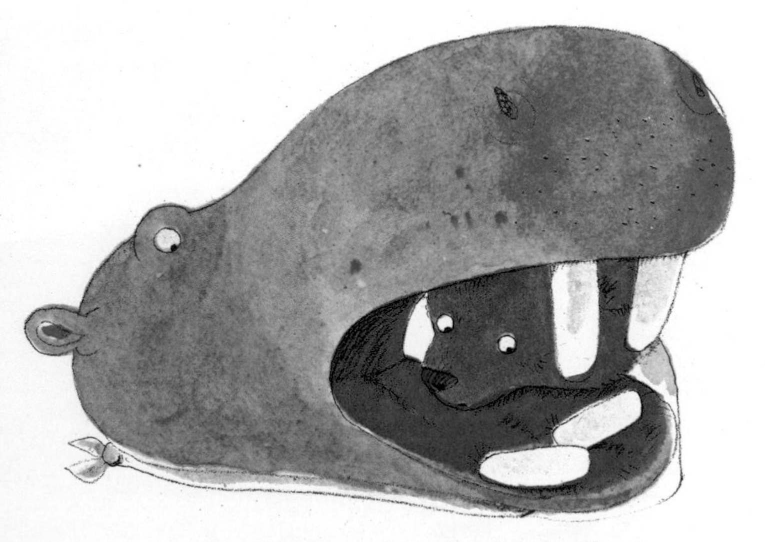

On Wednesday he looked at Hippopotamus' teeth.

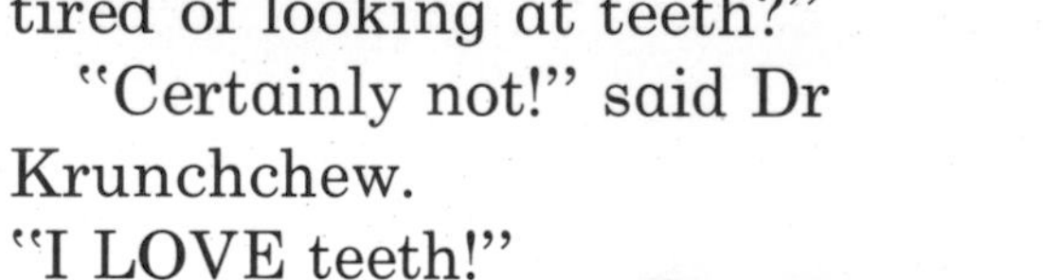

On Thursday, Walrus asked Dr Krunchchew, "Don't you ever get tired of looking at teeth?"

"Certainly not!" said Dr Krunchchew.
"I LOVE teeth!"

On Friday he cleaned a nice old Grandmother's teeth.

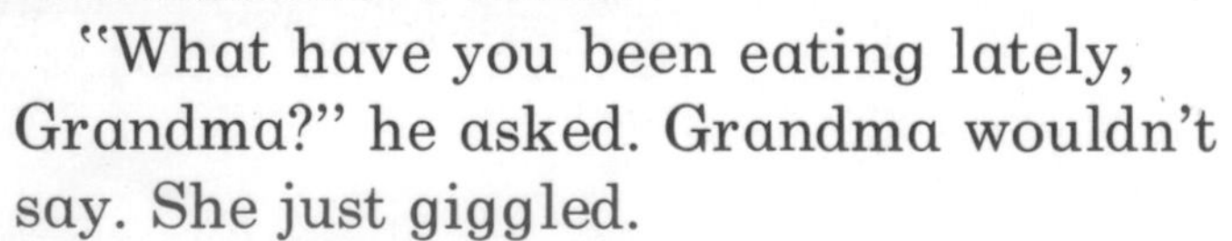

"What have you been eating lately, Grandma?" he asked. Grandma wouldn't say. She just giggled.

"Very fine molars you have, Mr Mole," laughed Dr Krunchchew on Saturday.

On Sunday Mrs Krunchchew said, "You have been looking at teeth all week. You need a rest. Go and look at something different. Why don't you go to the Natural History Museum and look at birds and flowers and other things?"

So Dr Krunchchew went to the museum, and looked at birds and flowers . . . and . . .

. . . and other things.

Nursery Rhyme Time

Old Mother Hubbard
Went to the cupboard
To fetch her poor dog a bone;
But when she got there
The cupboard was bare,
And so the poor dog had none.

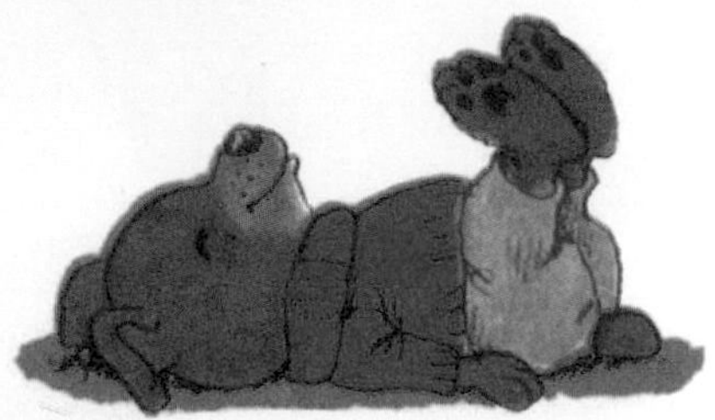

She went to the baker's
To buy him some bread;
But when she came back
The poor dog was dead

She went to the undertaker's
To buy him a coffin;
But when she came back
The poor dog was laughing.

She took a clean dish
To get him some tripe;
But when she came back
He was smoking a pipe.

She went to the grocer's
To buy him some fruit;
But when she came back
He was playing the flute.

She went to the tailor's
To buy him a coat;
But when she came back
He was riding a goat.

She went to the hatter's
To buy him a hat;
But when she came back
He was feeding the cat.

She went to the barber's
To buy him a wig;
But when she came back
He was dancing a jig.

She went to the cobbler's
To buy him some shoes;
But when she came back
He was reading the news.

She went to the seamstress
To buy him some linen;
But when she came back
The dog was a-spinning.

She went to the hosier's
To buy him some hose;
But when she came back
He was dressed in his clothes.

The dame made a curtsey,
The dog made a bow;
The dame said, "Your servant,"
The dog said, "Bow-wow."

Glip and Glop, the Greek Painters

Mrs Metropolus asked Glip and Glop to come and paint her house.

She didn't care what colours they painted it on the inside. But she did insist that the outside of the house be painted blue and white.

She asked Glip and Glop to mind her little boy, Percy, while she went shopping.

"Remember! Paint the outside blue and white," she said as she left.

Glip painted the living room.
It was beautiful.

Glop painted a funny wolf
on Percy's bedroom wall.

They both painted a happy sun on the dining-room ceiling.

And when they had finished painting the inside of the house they went outside to paint the outside of the house.

"Don't forget . . . blue and white," Glip said to Glop.

Glip painted two sides of the house blue and white.

And Glop painted two sides of the house blue and white.

Oh look what they have done! They have painted the house blue and white all right. But half the house has blue sides with white windows, and the other half has white sides with blue windows.

Mrs Metropolus would be furious.

But when Mrs Metropolus came home, she was very pleased. "Why, it is just like having two houses," she said.

That night she gave Percy a bath.

The Bear Twins get Dressed

Brother Bear woke up one cold, frosty morning. He wanted to dress very warmly before he went outside.

He yawned and got up out of bed.

He took off his pyjamas and left them on the floor. Naughty bear!

slippers

pyjama top

pyjam botto

He put on his

underwear

cap

shirt

trousers

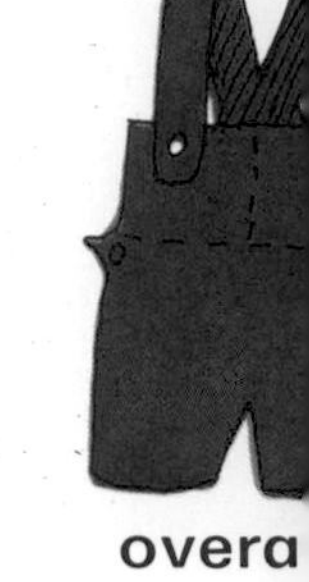

overa

tie

sweater

socks

hat

scarf

plimsolls

glove

jacket

overcoat

raincoat

and sou'wester

As he was walking out of the front door his Mother said, "Don't forget to put your boots on!"

boots

Sister Bear got up out of bed.

She took off her pretty nightdress
and put it away neatly. Nice bear!

nightdress

She put on her

knickers

petticoat

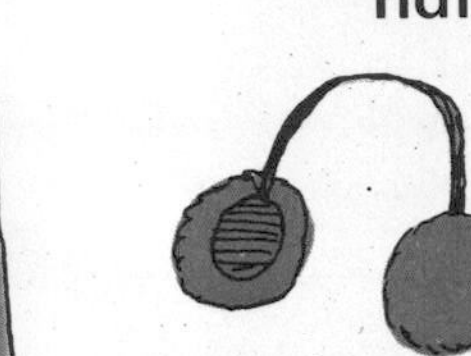

hair ribbon

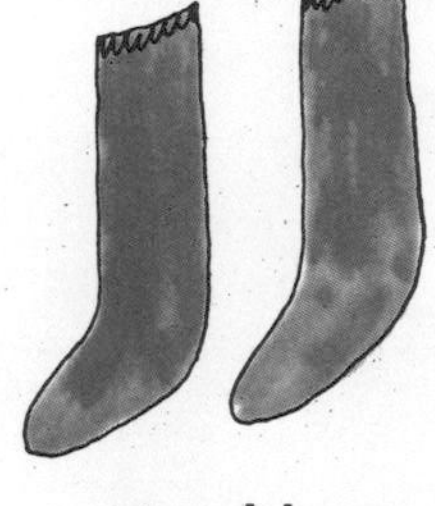

ear muffs

blouse

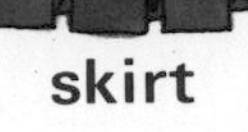

skirt

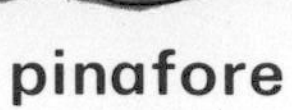

pinafore

stockings

shoes

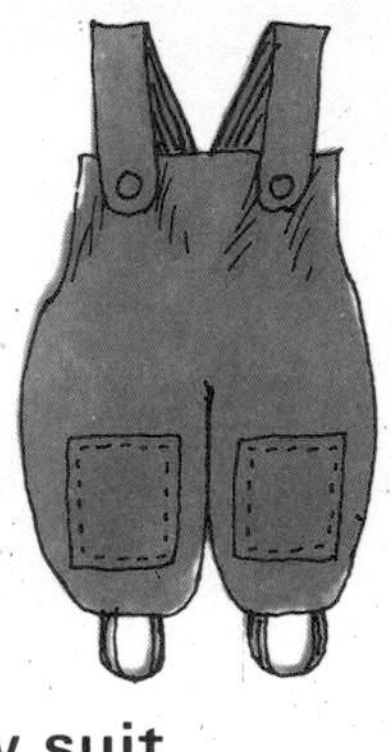

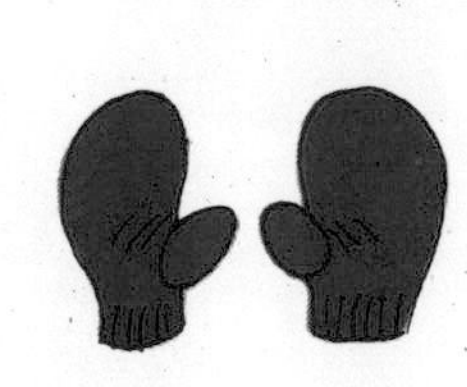

snow suit

and mittens.

She put her

handkerchief

and purse

in her handbag.

As she was walking out of
the front door her mother said,
"Don't forget to put your boots on!"

Do you ever forget
to put on your boots?

Nursery Rhyme Time

Little Boy Blue,
  Come blow your horn!
The sheep's in the meadow,
  The cow's in the corn.

Where is the boy
  who looks after the sheep?
He's under the haycock,
  Fast asleep.

Will you wake him?
  No, not I,
For if I do,
  He's sure to cry.

Professor Dig and his Egyptian Mummy

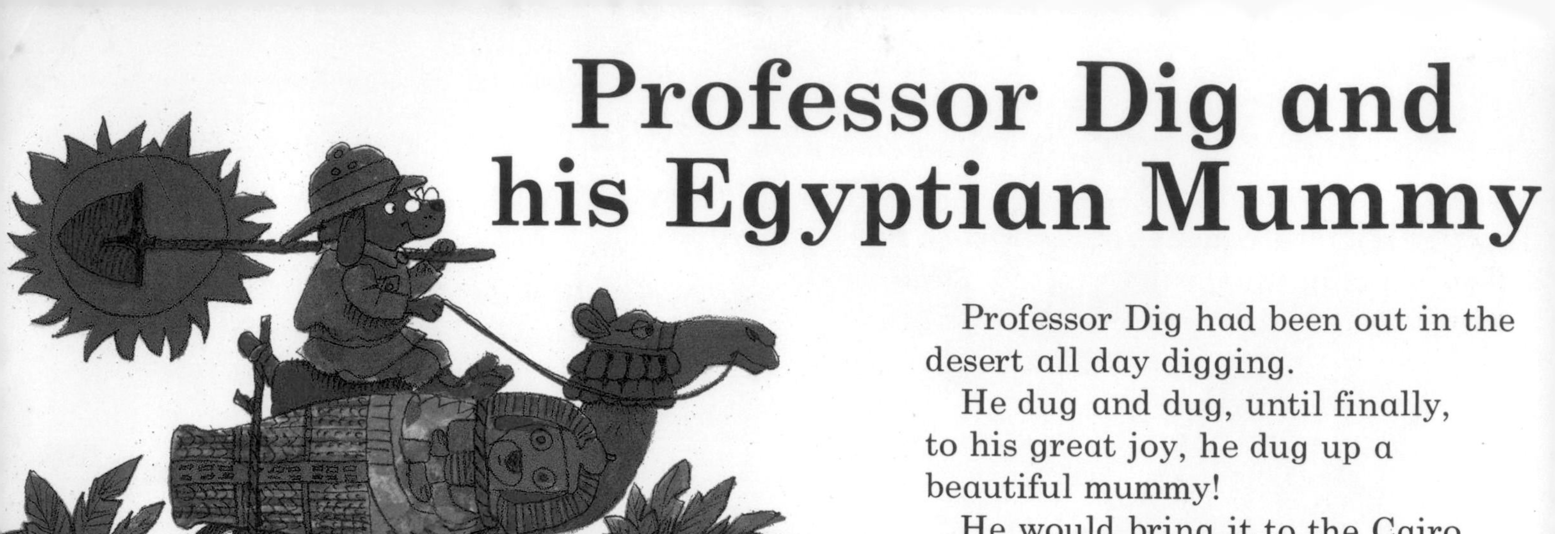

Professor Dig had been out in the desert all day digging.

He dug and dug, until finally, to his great joy, he dug up a beautiful mummy!

He would bring it to the Cairo museum where everyone could come and look at it and say "OOH! AAH!!"

It was *so* beautiful!

The Professor was very hot and thirsty when he arrived in Cairo.

He decided that he would stop at Ali Baba's restaurant to have cold lemonade.

"Will you watch my mummy for a few minutes while I sit and drink a cold glass of lemonade?" the Professor asked Ali Baba.

Now, Ali Baba couldn't see very well. He thought that the professor's MUMMY was the Professor's real live MOTHER!!

"What kind of a son is that who will leave his mother standing after a hot trip while he sits down and has a cold lemonade?" Said Ali to the mummy, "You must be very tired. Permit me to sit you in a chair."

Ali Baba put the mummy in the chair. "Oh your poor woman," said Ali. "You are so stiff from your long journey you can't even bend to sit down. Perhaps if you were to lie down with your feet in the air you would feel better.

"Ah, yes, I can see you are looking better already," he said. "Your dress is a little dusty, though. Let me dust you off. Yes, you are looking much, much better.

"Ah, the music is playing in the Palm Room. Rum de dum de dum. May I have this dance while we are waiting for your son? Dum de dum. Ah, madam you are a delightful dancer."

Just then the Professor came along. He thanked Ali for taking care of his mummy and carried it away.

"Oh, how that boy treats his poor old mother," said Ali. "IMAGINE!! Carrying her on his head! I wouldn't treat my mummy that way. Would YOU?"

Sven Svenson's Busy Day

Sven Svenson lived with Mrs Sven Svenson, on a farm in Sweden. He ate a gherkin for breakfast.

He put on his straw hat and he went to the barn to milk his cow. His cow kicked over the milk pail.

He fed his hens and gathered their eggs.

He went to the railway station to pick up a package which was coming on the train from the city.

It was a present for his wife. He tried it on for fun.

When he got home, he gave the hat to his wife. She gave him a gherkin for lunch.

After lunch Sven brought the hay in from the fields. His cow loves to eat hay and straw.

He put the hay into the barn. The wind blew his straw hat up into the barn. He would climb up and get it after he had a drink of water. It was a hot day and he was dry and thirsty.

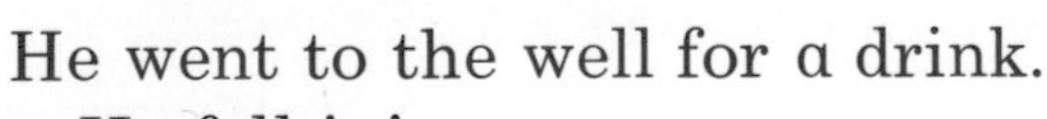

He went to the well for a drink.
He fell in!

Mrs Svenson came and pulled him out. Her new hat fell in the well.

It was the end of a busy day. Sven Svenson and Mrs Sven Svenson ate seven gherkins for supper.

Sven Svenson's cow found
Sven Svenson's hat in
Sven Svenson's barn.
Sven Svenson's cow ate
Sven Svenson's hat for supper.

Hark, hark,
The dogs do bark;
The beggars are coming to town.
Some in rags,
And some in tags,
And one in a velvet gown.

Nursery Rhyme Time

I would, if I could,
If I couldn't, how could I?
I couldn't, without I could, could I?
Could you, without you could, could ye?
Could ye? could ye?
Could you, without you could, could ye?

Jack and Jill went up the hill
To fetch a pail of water.
Jack fell down and broke his crown,
And Jill came tumbling after.

Up Jack got and home did trot,
As fast as he could caper,
To old Dame Dob, who patched his nob
With vinegar and brown paper.

There was an old woman
Lived under a hill,
And if she's not gone,
She lives there still.

Mamma Bear bakes a Cake

Mamma Bear wanted to enter the cooking contest at the Fair. First she read the recipe for the cake.

"Let's see," said Mamma. "I'll need some flour."

Mamma measured out the flour. Oh, Mamma, what a mess!

While the cake was baking, Mamma was setting out the cake plates.
"Quick, Mamma," cried Huckle, "I smell smoke."

Oh, Mamma! Hurry Mamma!

Oh, Mamma! Too late!

Poor Mamma Bear. Her cake was ruined. "Why not cover the burnt part with icing?" said Pappa. "It might *look* better."

Oh, Mamma, will you never pay attention? Now the icing has boiled over.

Well, Mamma finally finished her cake. It won last prize in the cooking contest. Better luck next time, Mamma!

Ukulele Louie, the Hawaiian Fisherman

Every day, Ukulele Louie threw his fishing net into the water.

And every day he pulled his net out of the water. It was always full of fish.

Then gaily singing and playing his ukulele, he took his fish and sold them to his good friend, Joe, who owned a restaurant.

"I wish I could be a cook in a restaurant instead of fishing every day," Louie said to Joe. "I could make all kinds of good things to eat. Yum Yum!"

"Very well," said Joe. "Put on this cook's hat, and go into the kitchen and see what you can cook up. I have to go out but I will be back in a few minutes. Just try to be neat."

Joe left and Louie went into the kitchen.

He put the fish in the refrigerator.
He knocked over the milk while he was taking out some eggs.

He poured a jar of vinegar into a bowl. He put two dozen eggs in the bowl, and beat them with a whisk.

He went to the sink to wash the whisk. He forgot to turn the tap off.

He tried to shake some ketchup into the bowl but it wouldn't come out. He shook and shook.
The ketchup came out.

He carried the bowl across the kitchen.
The door opened.

Joe had returned.
"I am afraid you will never be a good cook," said Joe. "You should have used apple sauce instead of ketchup."
"Yes. I think you are right," said Louie.

And so Ukulele Louie went back to fishing, and singing, and playing his ukulele, and he never wanted to cook anything ever again.

Nursery Rhyme Time

"Pussy cat, pussy cat, where have you been?"
"I've been to London to look at the queen."
"Pussy cat, pussy cat, what did you there?"
"I frightened a little mouse under her chair."

Cleaning-Up Time

Each of the animals has a job to do to make everything tidy around the house. What do you think each animal is about to do?

Don't you think some of them should be thrown in the dustbin?

Angus, the Scottish Bagpiper

When Officer Angus said "Stop!" people heard him and they stopped!

He told the cars to *STOP* so that the Macintosh family could cross the street. The cars stopped.

He told two silly boys to *stop fighting*.
The silly boys stopped.

He told Sandy to please *STOP DANCING* on the grass.
Sandy stopped.

He had spent a busy day telling people to stop doing something. Now he was going to go home and have fun playing his bagpipes.

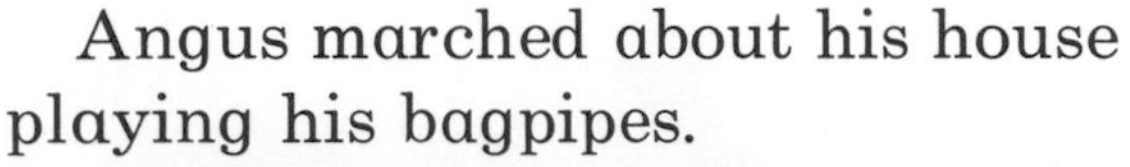

Angus marched about his house playing his bagpipes.

"SCREECH SCREECH OOOHAAAH OOOOHAAAAAH!"

Oh such a horrible ferocious noise he made.

"NYANNGGGG NYANNGGGG NYANNGGGGGGGG!"

The sound of his bagpipes could be heard all over town.

"Angus, please STOP!" all the people cried. But Angus was playing so loudly he couldn't hear. And the longer he played the louder he played, and the bigger his bagpipes swelled up.

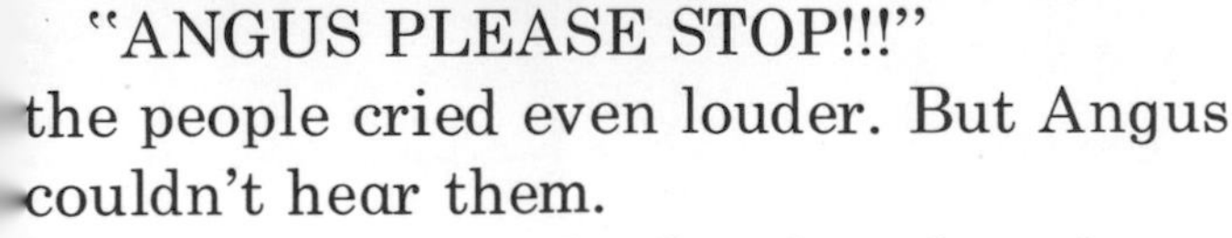

"ANGUS PLEASE STOP!!!" the people cried even louder. But Angus couldn't hear them.

Louder and louder he played, and bigger and BIGGER his bagpipes grew.

"ANGUS,PLEASE STOP!!!!" the people roared.

Fortunately for the townspeople, the bagpipes burst, and Angus STOPPED.

Little Jack Horner
Sat in the corner,
Eating a Christmas pie;
He put in his thumb,
And pulled out a plum,
And said, "What a good boy am I!"

Three wise men of Gotham,
They went to sea in a bowl;
If the bowl had been stronger,
My song would have been longer.

Nursery Rhyme Time

Three blind mice, see how they run!
They all run after the farmer's wife,
Who cut off their tails with a carving knif
Did you ever see such a thing in your life,
As three blind mice?

Jack Sprat could eat no fat,
His wife could eat no lean,
And so between them both, you see,
They licked the platter clean.

There was a little girl, and she had a little curl
Right in the middle of her forehead;
When she was good, she was very, very good,
But when she was bad she was horrid.

Goosey, goosey gander,
Where shall I wander?
Upstairs and downstairs
And in my lady's chamber.

The Silly Polish Farmers

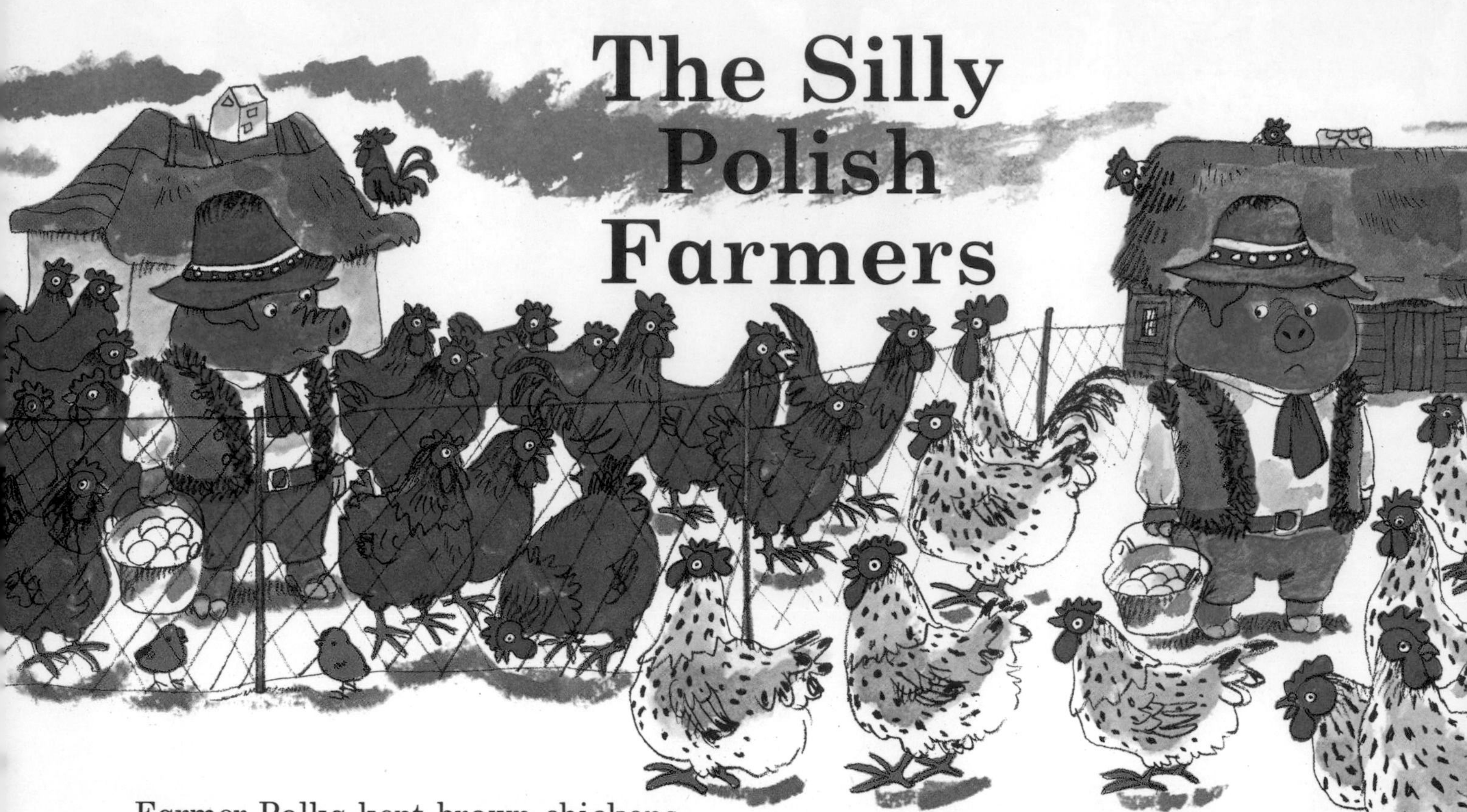

Farmer Polka kept brown chickens. He thought they laid better eggs than spotted chickens.

Farmer Dotta lived next door. He kept spotted chickens because he thought they laid better eggs than brown chickens.

Polka and Dotta spent all their time arguing when it would have been better for them if they spent their time working or playing games together.

One day they were arguing as usual.
"My hens lay better eggs than yours," said Polka Pig.
They both put down their pails . . .
. . . and they started to fight!

Oh, those silly pigs!

They fought and they fought.

And when those silly pigs could fight no more they stopped.

They went to pick up their pails of eggs but they couldn't tell which belonged to whom, for the eggs in both pails were exactly alike.

"How silly we have been," they both said. "Let us work and play together and always be friends."

Well, you should see those farmers today. They took down the fence between their farmyards. They now have brown chickens, red chickens, black chickens, white chickens, spotted chickens, all kinds of chickens. They even have an ostrich! And they all lay exactly the same eggs. Well—*almost all* of them do.

HOTEL
GENERAL STORE
COWBOY SUITS
BOOTS
BANK
TOWN HALL
street lamp
hitching post
gold miner
donkey
money box
cowboy
sheriff
locomotive
headlight
BUFFALO BILL
wheel
stagecoach

Out West
Indian is coming to town to buy a horse for his squaw to ride. Why do you think it would be nice for her to have a horse to ride?
covered wagon
BLACKSMITH
saddle
oxen
Indian
papoose
horseshoe
squaw
FEED
AND
barrel
lasso
cattle truck
horse
tender
cattle
corral

Baa, baa, black sheep,
Have you any wool?
Yes, sir, yes, sir,
Three bags full;
One for my master,
And one for my dame,
And one for the little boy
Who lives down the lane.

Nursery Rhyme Time

Little Polly Flinders
Sat among the cinders,
Warming her pretty little toes;
Her mother came and caught her,
And whipped her little daughter
For spoiling her nice new clothes.

Sing a song of sixpence,
A pocket full of rye;
Four and twenty blackbirds
Baked in a pie!

When the pie was opened,
The birds began to sing.
Wasn't that a dainty dish
To set before the king?

The king was in his counting-house,
Counting out his money;
The queen was in the parlour,
Eating bread and honey.

The maid was in the garden,
Hanging out the clothes;
When down came a blackbird
And pecked off her nose!

Schmudge, the German Chimney Sweep

Schmudge cleaned the soot from chimneys and quite naturally he got very dirty every day. He looked like a little cloud of black smoke as he walked down the street.

He came to Frau Wascherwommen's house to clean her chimney. She just loved to have things clean. Why, she had just done her washing and was putting it out to dry.

"Oh, goody," she said. "Go up to the roof, but don't you dare put any paw prints on my clean walls!"

Schmudge walked up to the roof. The Frau's little boy, Hans, followed him.

Schmudge walked out onto the roof and looked to see how dirty the chimney was. It was very dirty!

Little Hans couldn't see where he was going.

"ACHTUNG!!" shouted a boy who was passing by on his bicycle. "ACHTUNG!! LOOK OUT!!"

Oh, too late! Little Hans
had slipped and fallen!

Brave Schmudge leaped after him
. . . and caught him!!

Down, down they fell . . . into
Frau Wascherwommen's clean white
washing!

Frau Wascherwommen came running
out of her kitchen.

"You have ruined my washing,"
she shrieked.

But when she saw that Schmudge
had saved her little Hans she didn't
care.

Schmudge went home . . .

. . . and took a bath!

Ernst, the Swiss Mountain Climber

Ernst Goat could climb up mountains. He could climb down mountains, too.

Heidi Goat had a cow who could climb up mountains. But her cow couldn't climb down.

One day when Ernst was playing his long alphorn Heidi came running and said, "My cow has climbed the mountain again!"

Ernst climbed up the mountain.

"This is the last time I will bring Heidi's cow down from the mountain," he said.

He tied a rope around the cow and started to lower her to the meadow below.

Suddenly he slipped! . . .

. . . and fell!!!!

Ernst caught a branch with his axe just in time.

"I will never again climb that mountain to bring your cow down," he said.

The very next day, Heidi came to Ernst and said, "My cow has climbed the mountain again!"

Ernst grabbed his rope and axe.

"This is the last time I will bring your cow down from the mountain," he said.

I wonder if it was?

Nursery
Rhyme Time

Wee Willie Winkie runs through the town,
Upstairs and downstairs, in his nightgown.
Rapping at the window, crying through the lock
"Are the children all in their beds, for now it's eight o'clock?"

Good night,
Sleep tight,
Wake up bright
In the morning light
To do what's right
With all your might.